BRYAN ADAMS

EXCLUSIVE DISTRIBUTORS:
MUSIC SALES LIMITED
8/9 FRITH STREET, LONDON W1V 5TZ, ENGLAND
MUSIC SALES PTY. LIMITED
120 ROTHSCHILD STREET, ROSEBERRY, NSW 2018, AUSTRALIA

MUSIC SALES' COMPLETE CATALOGUE LISTS THOUSANDS OF TITLES
AND IS FREE FROM YOUR LOCAL MUSIC SHOP, OR DIRECT FROM
MUSIC SALES LIMITED. PLEASE SEND A CHEQUE OR POSTAL ORDER
FOR £1.50 FOR POSTAGE TO MUSIC SALES LIMITED,
NEWMARKET ROAD, BURY ST. EDMUNDS, SUFFOLK IP33 3YB.

THIS BOOK © COPYRIGHT 1986 BY
WISE PUBLICATIONS
UK ISBN 0.7119.0793.5
UK ORDER NO. AM61474

DESIGNED BY PEARCE MARCHBANK
COMPILED BY PETER EVANS

WISE PUBLICATIONS
LONDON/NEW YORK/SYDNEY

CUTS LIKE A KNIFE
PAGE 9

(EVERYTHING I DO) I DO IT FOR YOU
PAGE 40

HEAVEN
PAGE 30

THE ONLY ONE
PAGE 4

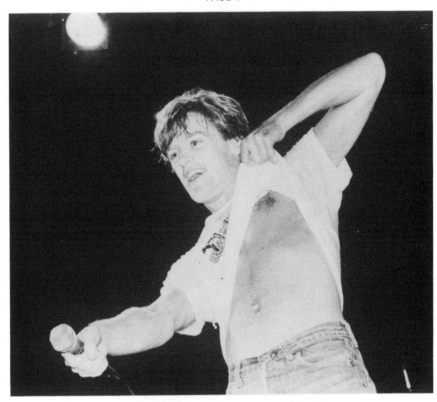

RUN TO YOU
PAGE 21

SOMEBODY
PAGE 36

STRAIGHT FROM THE HEART
PAGE 26

SUMMER OF '69
PAGE 44

THIS TIME
PAGE 16

THE ONLY ONE

WORDS & MUSIC: BRYAN ADAMS AND JIM VALLANCE

Moderate rock ♩ = 138

1. Well, I made up my mind,— not going to let you get __ a-way. Yeah, to think that I'm __ the luck-y guy,__ well, I've

2. Last night, well, I thought you might __ have stayed. If I'd have had the guts __ I would have pushed my luck,__ but then you

al - most got ___ it made. 'Cause it's been so long ___ since I've felt ___
might have turned ___ a - way. How do I ex - plain? ___ I know it
(3rd time instrumental)

___ this strong ___ a - bout an - y - one ___ at all. ___ I get
sounds in - sane, ___ but I've been through this ___ be - fore. ___ In just a

so ex - cit - ed, I ain't going to fight ___ it, I
mat - ter of time, ___ you could change your mind; ___ you could

CUTS LIKE A KNIFE

WORDS & MUSIC: BRYAN ADAMS AND JIM VALLANCE

1.Driv - in' home__ this eve - ning, I could of sworn__ we had it all worked out.__

You

had this boy ____ be - liev - in' way be -yond ___ the shad - ow of a doubt. ___

2. Then I

heard it on ___ the street; ___ I heard you might ___ of found ___ some -bod -y new. ___

3. *(See additional lyrics)*

Well,

who ___ is he, ba - by? Who is he ___ and tell ___ me what he means to

you? 4. I

took it all ___ for grant - ed, but how was I ___ to know ___ that

you'd be let - ting go? Now it cuts like a

To Coda ⊕

knife.___

(Instr. Solo ad lib)

2.   D.S.S. al Coda 𝄉𝄉

Coda

(End Solo)   4. I

knife,   but it feels so

descresc.   mp

right.___   And it cuts like a   knife,

and it feels so_____ right.____

cresc. poco a poco

Na na na_____ na na

na na na____ na na.

Repeat ad lib and fade

G   C(add2)   D   G   C(add2)

Verse 3:
There's times I've been mistaken;
There's times I thought I'd been misunderstood.
So wait a minute darlin'.
Can't you see we did the best we could?
This wouldn't be the first time
Things have gone astray.
Now you've thrown it all away.
(To Chorus:)

THIS TIME

WORDS & MUSIC: BRYAN ADAMS AND JIM VALLANCE

no way __ she's gon-na get a-way. This time __ ev-

-'ry-thing is eas-y, an-y day, _(4th time)_ I'm I'm gon-na make her

1. mine.

2.5. I'm gon-na make her mine.

3. D.S. 𝄋

To next strain

4. It's gon-na make her mine. D.S. 𝄋 hard to take, __ 'cause she's

miles a-way, ___ and I've wait-ed a long ___ time. But the

feel-ing is right, ___ dar-ling, one of these nights, ___ yeah, ___

___ I'm gon-na let you know. ___ Oh; _____

RUN TO YOU

WORDS & MUSIC: BRYAN ADAMS AND JIM VALLANCE

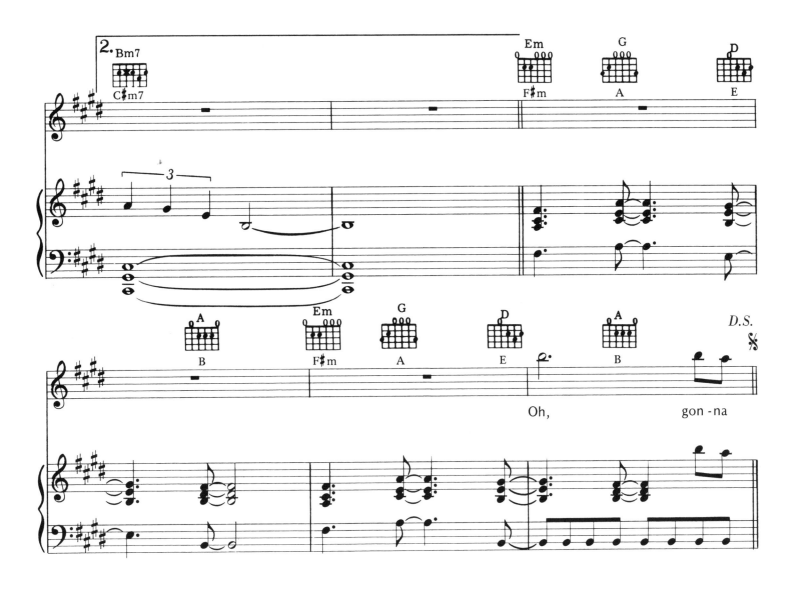

Verse 2:
She's got a heart of gold,
She'd never let me down.
But you're the one that always turns me on
And keep me comin' 'round.
I know her love is true,
But it's so damn easy makin' love to you.
I got my mind made up,
I need to feel your touch.

(To Chorus:)

STRAIGHT FROM THE HEART

WORDS & MUSIC: BRYAN ADAMS AND ERIC KAGNA

it's com-in' straight from the heart.

HEAVEN

WORDS & MUSIC: BRYAN ADAMS AND JIM VALLANCE

I've been wait-ing for___ so long for some-thing___ to ar-rive;___

for love___ to come a-long.___ Now our dreams are com-in' true,___

___ through the good times and the bad.___ Yeah, I'll be stand-in' there___ by___ you.

D.S.S.

And

Instrumental solo - - - - - - -*end solo*

33

SOMEBODY

WORDS & MUSIC: BRYAN ADAMS AND JIM VALLANCE

1. I been look-in' for some - one
2. Now who can you turn _____ to

Verse 3:
When you're out on the front line
And you're watchin' them fall,
It doesn't take long to realize
It ain't worth fightin' for.

Verse 4:
I thought I saw the Madonna
When you walked in the room.
Well your eyes were like diamonds,
And they cut right through,—oh they cut right through.

(To Chorus:)

(EVERYTHING I DO) I DO IT FOR YOU

WORDS & MUSIC: BRYAN ADAMS/R.J. LANGE/M. KAMEN

for,   you can't tell me it's not worth dy - in'

for.   You know it's true _____ ev - ery - thing I

do,   I do it for ___ you.

2.

There's no love like your love and no

oth - er could give more ___ love, there's no - where ___ un - less

you're there   all the   time,_____ all the   way___   yeah._____

Oh   you can't

tell   me   it's not worth try - in'   for,   I can't

help_____ it, there's no - thin' I want   more.   Yeah___ I would

fight for you,____ I'd lie____ for you,____ walk the wire for you,____ yeah____ I'd die for____ you.____ You know it's true, ev - ery-thing I do, oh,_____ ____ I do it for____ you.

VERSE 2:
Look into your heart
You will find there's nothin' there to hide
Take me as I am, take my life
I would give it all, I would sacrifice.

Don't tell me it's not worth fightin' for
I can't help it, there's nothin' I want more
You know it's true, everything I do
I do it for you.

SUMMER OF '69

WORDS & MUSIC: BRYAN ADAMS AND JIM VALLANCE

Moderately Bright ♩ = 138

I got my first real six-string; _ bought _ it at the five and dime; played _ it 'til my fin-gers_bled; was the sum-mer of

Verse:

six-ty nine. 1. Me ___ and some guys from school had a band and we tried real hard. Jim-my quit and Jo-dy got mar-ried; ___ I should-a known we'd nev-er get far. Oh, when I look back now, ___ that sum-mer seemed to

45

Verse 2:
Ain't no use in complainin' when you got a job to do.
Spent my evenin's down at the drive-in, and that's when I met you.
Standin' on your mama's porch, you told me that you'd wait forever.
Oh, and when you held my hand, I knew that it was now or never.
Those were the best days of my life.

Verse 3:
And now the times are changin'; look at everything that's come and gone.
Sometimes when I play that old six-string I think about you; wonder what went wrong.
Standin' on your mama's porch, you told me it'd last forever.
Oh, and when you held my hand, I knew that it was now or never.
Those were the best days of my life.

Printed and bound in Great Britain by
Caligraving Limited Thetford Norfolk

12/01 (42158)